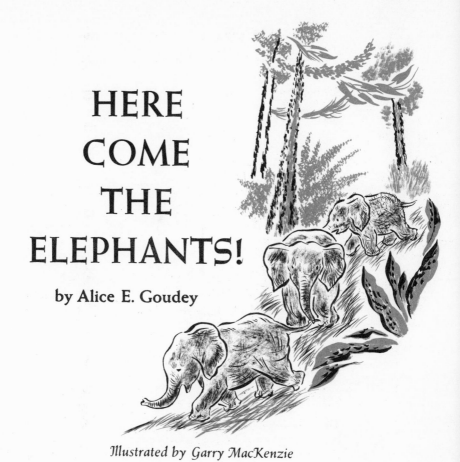

HERE
COME
THE
ELEPHANTS!

by Alice E. Goudey

Illustrated by Garry MacKenzie

Charles Scribner's Sons   **New York**

29,941

To Billy

We are grateful to Lee S. Crandall,
General Curator Emeritus of the New York Zoological Society,
for reading and checking the text of this book.

THE AFRICAN ELEPHANTS

THE AFRICAN ELEPHANTS

Little Elephant looks out on his new world from a safe place beneath his mother's big, warm body.

He can feel her swaying gently from side to side. He can hear the low, contented rumble that comes from her throat as if she were singing an ancient elephant lullaby to him.

Two days ago he was born beneath an acacia tree whose rounded top and drooping branches shelter him from the hot African sun like a great parasol.

3

Little Elephant was born in the north-eastern part of Tanganyika, a country on the continent of Africa. It is a place of grass-covered savannas, dotted here and there with groves of trees and thorny bushes. Along the rivers are dense forests, and in the distance one can see Mt. Kilimanjaro peaked with snow.

Standing beside his mother, Little Elephant looks very small but what a large "baby" he is!

Who, but a big elephant mother, would have a baby that weighs almost two hundred pounds!

And who, but an elephant mother, would have a baby that is almost as tall as yardstick!

A thin coat of soft, black fuzz covers his

body and little wisps of hair stand up on his head. His small trunk is like an overgrown nose and he curls it back out of the way as he drinks his mother's milk.

When night comes, cool air spreads across the African plains. Heavy dew settles on the grass and sparkles like a million diamonds in the tropic moonlight. The bright stars, in the darkness of the sky, seem so near that one could reach up and touch them.

Little Elephant hears the night cries of many animals. He hears the snarl of a leopard and the long, drawn-out wail of a hyena. He hears the mighty roar of a lion that seems to shake the very earth. And then he hears the clatter of many hoofs as the antelope and the zebra dash across the plains.

But no animal will attack Little Elephant as long as he stays close to his mother, for she has no enemies except man.

Now and then Mother caresses him with her trunk. And so they pass the night.

Mother Elephant does not leave her child for a moment. For the first few days she eats only what she can find close by. And she has no need to go for water as she has a large storage tank in her stomach which she can draw upon.

On the second day of his life Little Elephant can stand on his thick, straight, stubby legs and take a few wobbly steps. His front feet are round and shaped like English muffins, but his hind feet are an oval shape.

Strange as it may seem, he really walks on the tips of his toes but you cannot see them at all because they are hidden in thick pads of flesh. Around the edges of his muffin-feet are toenails which look new and shiny as all new baby toenails look.

In a few days Little Elephant can walk well enough to leave his birthplace under the acacia tree. His mother guides him with her trunk on his first short journey.

It is not long before Little Elephant and his mother join a big herd of elephants browsing near the forest's edge. Of course it is the first time that he has seen his relatives and the other members of the herd.

There is Old Grandfather Elephant who looks very old indeed. His thick hide is criss-crossed with deep wrinkles. His enormous ears turn over at the tops and his skull is sunken at his temples. He is almost twice as tall as a six foot man and his yellowed ivory tusks seem too heavy for him to carry. He is the leader of the herd.

There is the Wicked One who waves his trunk about and trumpets loudly. He has small, red-rimmed eyes and when he looks at Old Grandfather they have a wicked gleam.

There is no doubt that he would like to be the leader of the herd.

There is Little Elephant's father who is a fine, big tusker with gentle eyes. He walks with pride and dignity, and looks as though he is very wise.

Little Elephant discovers that he has two plump sisters. Little Sister is five years old. Big Sister is sixteen years old.

There are the other gentle mothers with great grey faces and kind eyes who keep watch over their children and train them in the ways of elephants.

They all gather around Little Elephant and
make low rumbling noises and little squeaks
to welcome him.

He is the new member of the herd.

These big elephants of Africa are the largest animals that live on land. In all the world of animals only the whales that live in the sea are larger.

The mother elephants have small tusks but the big bulls have tusks so large that each of them may weigh more than a man. These tusks are their incisor teeth which have grown long. They are made of ivory and the elephants use them for fighting and for digging.

They have other teeth which they use for grinding food. These grinding teeth are almost a foot long and may weigh ten pounds each.

Their small eyes cannot see very far but

their trunks can catch the faintest odor carried by the wind.

Their long trunks look like noses that have stretched and stretched and stretched. They are really a part of their upper lips and cheeks, as well as their noses, that have grown together to make this long, hollow tube.

At the tip end their trunks have two small tabs, or "fingers." These make it easy for them to pick up the tiniest bits of anything.

Their trunks are very sensitive and can easily be hurt. It is a lucky thing that they can curl them up and keep them out of danger as an elephant would be helpless without his trunk. His neck is too short for him to reach up or down so he must depend upon his trunk to get water and gather food for him.

Little Elephant has not learned how to use his small trunk. As he goes about, the little thing flip-flaps from side to side.

One hot day the mosquitoes and the big grey flies settle on the backs and shoulders of the elephant children. They switch their tails over their backs. They fan their shoulders with their ears. But the pests zing and buzz and fly right back again.

The elephant mothers know just what to do. They suck up some water in their trunks and suddenly the little elephants feel wet and cool.

It is Little Elephant's first bath from Mother's "built-in" shower.

Then Mother scoops up some thin mud and plasters it on his head and back. This keeps the horrid blood-sucking insects from bothering him. But when the mud dries it, too, will make him feel itchy and then he will rub against a tree to get it off.

The elephants love the water. They draw it up in their trunks and then squirt it into their mouths. They splash about and spray themselves and spray each other until their wet hides look black and shining. They rumble and squeal and sometimes raise their trunks and trumpet loudly because they are having as much fun as children at a picnic.

When they finish bathing it is late and the blue-grey shadows of evening are creeping through the forest. Now the elephants are hungry and the children are squealing for their milk.

The elephants are almost always hungry. They spend most of their time cramming food into their mouths in order to fill up their big stomachs. Each one may eat several hundred pounds of food a day. They move about at night, while men are sleeping, to find new feeding grounds.

Elephants are not meat eaters. They kill no other animal for food. They eat leaves and roots and grass and bamboo shoots. They like coconuts and mangoes and wild fruits. They love bananas. And they like the things that men grow in their fields such as millet, corn, groundnuts, and sweet juicy sugar cane.

Now in the quiet of the darkness, the elephants do their noisy eating.

They curl their trunks around the branches high above their heads and break them off with a great splitting, cracking sound. They break off trees six inches thick.

They press their heads against much larger ones until the trees come toppling down. They pull the leaves off with their trunks and stuff them in their mouths. It sounds as if an army of giants is tearing up the forest.

Some of the elephants leave the herd when they have had enough to eat and go off into the forest, two by two. Big Sister and a proud, young tusker walk off together.

These are the sweethearts in the herd. They seem to be fond of one another and are kind and gentle.

In the shimmering moonlight Big Sister and the young tusker press their heads together. They twine their trunks together like lovers holding hands and make low, contented sounds as if they are whispering secrets to each other.

After the elephants have been eating for a while, Little Elephant hears a strange new noise. It is a rumbling noise like thunder. It seems to be all around him. It comes from inside his mother. It comes from inside Little Sister. And the biggest rumble of all comes from inside his big father.

It is the rumbling, growling sound their stomachs make as they digest their food. When their big stomachs all growl at once they make a terrible noise!

Little Elephant fills his stomach with about twenty quarts of milk each day. It takes a lot of milk to feed a baby that weighs two hundred pounds.

Little Elephant plays with the other small elephants in the herd. They have make-believe battles and push each other with their heads. They march about in single file holding onto one another's tails. They look as if they might be going to play the game of Crack the Whip.

One day they find a big ball of dirt which has been made by the ants. They have a great time pushing it around and squealing as small boys do when they play ball.

And then the time of year comes when no rain falls on this part of Africa. The streams dry up and the grass grows dry and brittle. The natives set fires to burn off the old dead grass to make way for the new grass when the rains come. Now the elephants must find food in some other place.

Late one afternoon Old Grandfather trumpets loudly and all the elephants come together in one big herd.

There is shrill trumpeting from the other bulls and the Wicked One trumpets loudest of all. He swings his head and acts as if he would like to chase Old Grandfather from the herd.

The mothers collect their children and at
last the elephants start on their long journey,
treading silently on their big, cushioned feet.

As they trek across the hot savanna the mothers fling up their trunks to test the air for the smell of their man-enemy. Little Elephant lags behind and his mother slaps his rump smartly with her trunk to teach him that he must stay within the herd.

Big-bodied grasshoppers and locusts with rasping wings rise up and spring aside from the elephants' path. Little Elephant hears the singing of the sun beetles and sees an ostrich racing across the plains with his fuzzy plumes dancing in the air.

He sees a buffalo with an egret riding on his back. He sees a hippopotamus, fat and portly. And he sees an old secretary bird walking sedately with his wing tips crossed behind his back like clasped hands. His

crested head makes him look like an old
bookkeeper with his quill pens stuck behind
his ears.

All night long the elephants travel toward the upper streams and the deep forest. When dawn shows in the eastern sky they raise their trunks and suck in the air. They catch the scent of water and travel on with long strides, as they are thirsty.

The watering hole is the gathering place for many animals, all seeking water in the early morning hours. Through the bush and across the plains many feet and wings are moving.

First come the birds, singing their songs of praise to the new day—the tufted shrikes, the weaver birds, and the golden orioles. An old baboon, scratching his head with his long finger, comes down a path, and a lioness with her cubs moves through the tall grass. The

eland, with corkscrew horns, the tiny dik-dik
with their spikey four-inch horns, the giraffe
with their tall, gawky babies, and the zebra
are all traveling toward the water.

Dawn finds many of them drinking from the watering hole.

And in the distance they see the elephants
arriving.

The elephants spray themselves and drink their fill of water and then again start on their journey. But during the mid-day heat they stop to rest and sleep in the shade of some acacia trees.

The grown-up elephants seldom lie down to sleep. But the babies fling themselves on the ground and sleep as soundly as puppies.

Some of the big elephants lean against the trees and close their eyes. But even while they sleep and doze there is constant movement in the herd. They sway and flap their fan-like ears and now and then a trunk goes up to test the air. Some of the mothers put their heads together and mumble like old ladies gossiping at a tea party.

Here there is no cooling water or mud to protect Little Elephant from the insects. So, when he wakens from his nap, Mother sucks up some dust in her trunk and blows it over him like a cloud of talcum powder.

During the second night of their journey the elephants stride along at a faster pace. They are in a hurry to reach their new feeding grounds. The little elephant children grow tired and hungry. They squeal for milk and make an awful racket, but their mothers do not stop. They urge their babies along with their trunks.

Little Elephant hangs onto his mother's tail and she pulls him along. This is much better than being pushed.

At dawn they reach a wide river which stretches before them like a rippling silver ribbon. A steep bank leads down to the river and here the elephants pause. Then they sit down and toboggan down the bank as if they were on sleds. What a noise they make as their big bodies hit the water and send it splashing in all directions!

Little Elephant tucks his hind legs under him. Whoops! Down he goes!

The elephants are fine swimmers and strike out for the opposite shore. Some of them swim with their heads above water and some of them swim with only their trunks sticking up like snaky periscopes.

Little Elephant swims on the upstream side of his mother so he will not be carried down stream by the current. Now and then Mother puts her trunk around him and draws him closer to her.

Beyond the river the herd follows a smooth road that leads them into the cool, green jungle where their journey ends.

Long ago elephants made this road by pushing down the trees. Big tuskers are as good as bulldozers when it comes to building roads through the tangled jungle. Down through the years the feet of many elephants, as well as those of other animals, have passed over this trail and kept it open like a well-traveled highway.

During the dry season the elephants stay in the forest near the river where they have food and water. And then there comes a day that brings a big change in the herd.

The Wicked One, without any warning, suddenly turns on Grandfather and drives his tusk into the old elephant's flank. Grandfather shrieks, and would like to fight the Wicked One, but he knows that he is too old to win a fight with the strong, young tusker.

Old Grandfather turns around and walks down the road all by himself. He looks like an old man in wrinkled, baggy trousers, suddenly grown tired. He does not turn to look back. He is leaving the herd forever.

Old Grandfather will find a quiet place away from the restless herd and there he will spend his remaining days. He may find other grandfathers who have left their herds and they will keep each other company.

These old elephants do not go to an "elephant cemetery" to die as many people think they do. They spend their last days wherever they are most likely to find food and water without traveling far.

Now that Old Grandfather has gone, there will be a new leader of the herd.

Both Father and the Wicked One step forward and trumpet shrilly. And then, with a piercing scream of rage, the Wicked One flourishes his trunk high in the air. He holds his enormous ears straight out, wide and stiff on each side of his head, and charges at Father like a full-rigged ship.

Father steps aside just in time to miss the sharp tusks of the Wicked One. Father, like most elephants, is peaceful and does not want to fight. And so the Wicked One becomes the leader of the herd.

It is not long now before the dry season is over and then, day after day, the rain pours from the darkened sky. The elephants do not like the noise of the rain falling on the leaves above them and leave the forest for the plains and bush country.

In a short time the grass is green again and tender shoots spring from the bushes.

But the Wicked One is not satisfied with this food. He has smelled the millet, the groundnuts, and the pumpkins in the natives' field, or *shamba*.

One evening he goes on a rampage and leads the younger, more inexperienced bulls in a raid. Father and Mother and the older members of the herd stand aside and will not go with him. They swing their trunks from side to side and make a rumbling noise as if to say, "Foolish One! You will come to no good end!"

Many years ago the herd raided a *shamba,* eating and trampling down the natives' crops. The wise ones still remember the shots that killed several of their members.

It may be that the Wicked One does not remember that sad day, because elephants, like human beings, sometimes do forget.

But the young bulls have never been on a raid before and do not know any better.

They are excited and go toward the *shamba* squealing and trumpeting. The natives hear them coming, smashing their way through the bushes and snapping off the branches in their way.

They shout, "Tembo! Tembo is coming!"

They quickly light torches and wave them in the air. They beat on gongs. They beat on drums and tin pans to frighten away the oncoming elephants. They know that if the elephants enter their fields their crops will be trampled flat and their harvest ruined.

But the wild elephants do not stop. They swing along at a rapid pace with their trunks waving and their big ears cocked.

When the raiders reach the *shamba* they lean their great weight against the posts that hold the fence and the posts go down like tenpins. They trample down the fence and begin their raid.

They pull up the millet and after beating the roots against their knees to free it of the dirt, they stuff it in their mouths. They smash the pumpkins with their feet and pick up the tiniest tidbits with their trunks. And they pull up the groundnuts which they love best of all. In a short time the field is ruined.

And then the Wicked One reaches up to yank the bananas from the trees.

Then Little Elephant hears the frightening sound of a shot. It is followed by a terrible scream from the Wicked One as he falls upon the ground. He tries to rise but falls again and then lies still.

Now there is panic among the young bulls who have foolishly followed him into danger. They bump into each other in their hurry to get away.

But again the shots ring out and one of the bulls feels a stinging pain in his foot. He takes a few steps and then goes down on his knees. Unlike a dog, he cannot walk far on three legs.

Even in their hurry to get away, the other elephants will not leave a wounded comrade. Two of them turn back. They lift him with their trunks and, pressing their bodies against him, one on each side, they help him leave the *shamba*.

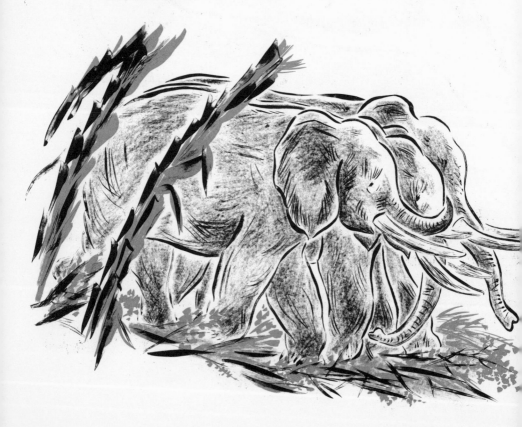

The wounded one bathes his foot and plasters mud on it. The wound will heal but he will carry the bullet in it all his life.

The wise ones among the young bulls will remember this bad experience. They will find food on the plains and in the forest and will leave man's food alone. It is sad that some must die in order that others learn this lesson. But man, too, must have food to live.

All of the elephants are frightened and want to get away from this place of danger. All night long they stride rapidly across the savanna like silent shadows.

Little Elephant never leaves his mother's side. The herd travels so fast that sometimes he has to hunch up his small back and take a few hurried steps to keep up.

Morning finds them entering a forest where the purple shadows and the tree trunks, so nearly the same color as their skins, will hide them. Here they will be safe.

Little Elephant has his breakfast of warm milk and then stretches out on the ground to sleep after his long journey. Mother stays close by to watch over him. She, too, shuts her eyes and sleeps, but even in her sleep she sways gently from side to side and moves her ears like big fans.

Father now becomes the leader of the herd. He is wise and gentle and will not lead the elephants into danger. The days to come will be happy, peaceful ones.

Little Elephant will grow about two inches each year. He will not grow up quickly as most wild animals do. He will have a long childhood and grow slowly as human children do. Maybe this long time for growth and learning is what makes an elephant so wise.

He will drink his mother's milk until he is about two years old. When he is five years old he will have small tusks. He will not be grown up until he is past twenty and will probably live about as long as most men live.

Little Elephant will have a better chance of

living a long life than many of his ancestors
had. Long before the birth of Christ, men
killed the elephants for the precious ivory in
their tusks.

The Bible says that King Solomon's navy
came "bringing gold, and silver, *ivory,* and
apes, and peacocks." King Solomon's
throne was made of ivory and overlaid with
gold.

Today we make piano keys, knife handles,
and delicate statues out of ivory.

But men are no longer allowed to kill the elephants by the thousands. In eastern Africa there are park-like places where they are safe, and a hunter must have a license to kill even one elephant unless the elephant is a raider.

Little Elephant will probably have a mate and children of his own. No doubt he will be a big tusker and the leader of the herd as his father and his grandfather before him were.

THE ASIAN ELEPHANTS

THE ASIAN ELEPHANTS

Bright colored parrots, with long tails and orange beaks, fly about in the tall trees of the jungle. A green pigeon whistles his song. And in the nut trees the squirrels and monkeys chatter and quarrel with one another.

Near the edge of the jungle a tiger creeps through the tall grass. The big, striped cat moves as quietly as a kitten. Only the slight stirring of the grass as he passes through tells that he is there.

The tiger knows that only a few hours ago a baby elephant was born in the Burmese jungle.

He lies down in the grass to wait for the time of night when even the insects have stopped their noisy singing and all is quiet. It is then that Mother Elephant will be most likely to take her soundest sleep.

Mr. Stripes, as the Burmese people call a tiger, does not dare to attack a big tusker. But Mother Elephant, like all female elephants of Asia, has no tusks. She is young and not full grown. Maybe Mr. Stripes can stampede her and drive her away. Then return quickly to attack her child.

He flicks the end of his tail back and forth
and spreads his claws as he watches Mother
fondle Little Elephant with her trunk.

There is not the slightest stirring of a breeze to carry the scent of the tiger to Mother Elephant. Slowly and stealthily he creeps through the jungle until he is behind her. He is not taking any chances of attacking her from the front and being flailed by her trunk.

He crouches low. And then, with outstretched claws and bared fangs, he springs upon her back. He sinks his fangs in her shoulder and with his hind feet he claws and rakes her back.

Mother Elephant screams in pain and fright. She rears up on her hind legs but the tiger sinks his claws still deeper. Screaming and trumpeting she charges through the jungle.

Little Elephant is left alone in the dark jungle. The frightened little fellow shuffles around in circles, screaming, screaming,

screaming for his mother as only a baby elephant can scream.

But it is not long before Mother Elephant returns to her child. On her back and sides are the cruel, bloody claw marks of the tiger.

The tiger lies farther back in the jungle. He has made his last attack. He was knocked from Mother's back by a low-hanging limb. And then she turned and trampled him until there was no life left in his striped body.

Mother runs her trunk over Little Elephant's head and back to see that he is not injured. She wraps her trunk around him and draws him close to her. In the night stillness he hears the toc-toc of the little bell that hangs around her neck.

The bells shows that Mother is not a wild elephant. It shows that she is an elephant who belongs to man.

This is the story of how Mother was captured and how she came to wear the bell.

When she was young she was a member of a herd of wild elephants which lived in the great jungles of Burma, on the continent of Asia.

One day, when she was about fifteen years old, the big tuskers in the herd became uneasy. They flapped their leathery ears and waved their trunks to test the air for the man-smell. Then the leader of the herd gave a shrill trumpeting scream of warning.

The man-smell came from three directions!

The elephants could hear men's voices shouting in the distance. They could hear the beating of gongs and the boom-boom of drums. They could hear the sharp noise of clappers made from hollow bamboo stems. And now and then a shot was fired.

As they listened with stiffened ears, the noise came closer. It seemed to be closing in around them.

Only one way lay open for their escape and that was straight ahead. At a signal from the leader they stampeded through the jungle, squealing and trumpeting and raising a great cloud of dust.

Other animals fled from the path of the elephants. Wild pigs, grunting and squealing, scuttled away with tails held high. A sambur deer bounded past. And a big buffalo thundered by.

Hour after hour the elephants fled through the jungle but never were they able to get away from the noise that followed them.

The babies wrapped their trunks around their mothers' tails and did their best to keep up.

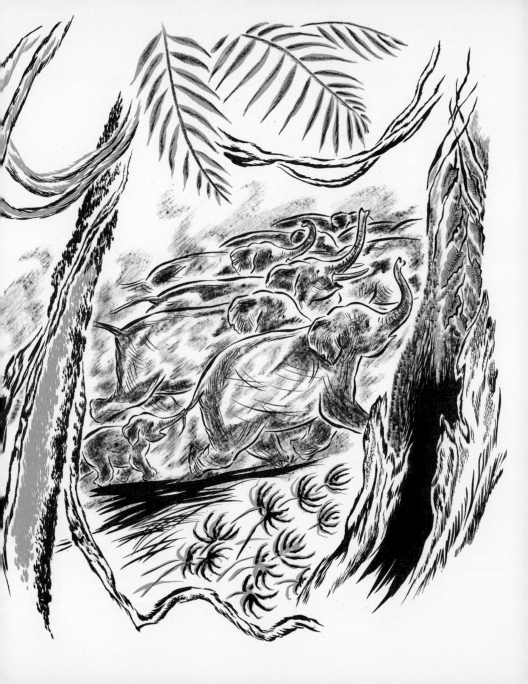

But when night came they stopped to rest and let the babies nurse.

And then they saw the gleam of fires all through the woods. They flared up on both sides and back of them, hemming them in.

Men sat quietly around the fires, now and then putting fresh logs on to keep them burning.

Fear kept the elephants from making a break for freedom. When one brave tusker tried to charge through the lines of fire and men, a flaming torch was thrust toward his face and he swerved back to join the herd.

But they were too worried to rest for long. Before midnight they pressed on between the lines of fire.

They traveled all through the night in this terrifying jungle that was no longer theirs. Dawn found them marching as fast as the young ones could go.

And then, without any warning, the noise burst forth again. Men yelled and shouted and fired shots into the air. There was the rumble of drums, the clang of gongs, and the noise of clappers.

The panic-stricken elephants rushed forward. Then suddenly they found themselves inside a strong pen.

A gate slammed shut behind them!

They were the prisoners of the shouting men.

They rushed madly to and fro trying to find a way to escape, but it was no use.

The pen in which the elephants were caught was called a *keddah*. It was made of large tree trunks sunk deep in the ground and bound together with heavy ropes. It was high and strong. When the elephants tried to break through, the men outside shouted and thrust their torches toward them.

Soon, tame elephants with men riding on their necks came through the gate. Four of them surrounded Mother. They pressed their bulky bodies so close to her that she could not move. Then a man crawled under the tame elephants and slipped a rope around each of Mother's legs and she was taken from the pen.

They tied her legs to four trees and there she was, held fast.

She struggled and twisted and fought to break the ropes that bound her. She raised her trunk and trumpeted and screamed with rage.

Other elephants in the herd were captured in this same way. But the grandfather elephants who were too old to work and the mothers with young babies were allowed to go back to the jungle.

After a while Mother gave up struggling although her small eyes still flashed with rage.

When she had become quiet, a slim, brown boy came and squatted on the ground near her.

"Wah!" he said, softly. "You are as beautiful as the new day!"

Then he talked to her quietly and told her he meant no harm. He offered her a banana and some juicy sugar cane.

This was the beginning of Mother's friendship with the slim, brown Burmese

boy. In time she came to know the sound of
his voice and the way he smelled. She liked
the tidbits that he fed her and she learned to
trust him.

The boy became her *oozie,* as the boys who ride the elephants are called. He helped to train her to drag logs in the teak forest and she became fond of him in the same way a horse or dog becomes fond of his master.

When the day's work was done, he let her have her freedom in the jungle to find food for herself. But first he hobbled her with a chain around her front legs so she would not go too far away.

The oozie hollowed out a bell from a piece of teak wood and fashioned clappers to hang on each side of it. The toc-toc of the bell tells him where to find her in the mornings. And this is how Mother came to belong to man and wear the little bell.

On the morning after Little Elephant is

born the oozie finds Mother with the claw marks of the tiger on her back. He puts medicine on the wounds to heal them.

He is proud of Little Elephant and says, "Wah! Some day you will be a fine, big tusker."

Now, as the days pass, Little Elephant comes to know and trust Mother's oozie. He follows him about like a puppy and eats rice and sweet tamarind fruit from his hand.

In the mornings he hears the oozie singing as he comes through the jungle. The oozie sings and talks to let Mother know that he is coming. He knows that it is dangerous to startle an elephant even though she has been trained.

When the oozie hears the little bell he calls,

*"Digo lah! Digo lah! (*Come here! Come here!)"

But Mother does not hurry. She takes her time while the oozie waits patiently for her to come.

When she finally goes to him, the oozie says, *"Hmit! (*Sit down!)" in a firm voice. Mother sits down on her haunches and then sinks to the ground with all four legs extended. When the oozie comes close to her he says, *"Tah! (*Get up!)." Mother stands up and he unfastens the fetter chains. Then he orders her to sit down again. This time he climbs on her head and off they go.

Little Elephant follows close behind as they make their way to the elephant camp. Maybe the oozie will give him some sweet sugar cane for breakfast.

During the day Mother works in the jungle dragging logs. The logs were once tall teak wood trees. They were cut down to make lumber for the decks of ships and for building furniture.

"*Yoo! Yoo! Yoo!* (Pull! Pull! Pull!)," calls the oozie. Mother leans forward and pulls the heavy log. She drags it down the jungle trail to the river.

Then, with her trunk, she moves first one end of the log and then the other until it is ready to roll down the bank. She pushes it with her foot. And down it goes into the river with a great splash!

The log will float down the river to the saw mill where it will be made into lumber.

Other elephants and their oozies work in the jungle. Big bull elephants push and lift the logs with their tusks and trunks.

When the day's work is finished, the oozies bathe the elephants in the river. They scrub them with the bark of a tree which makes a foamy lather.

Little Elephant, too, takes his bath. He gives himself a good shower.

The elephants who live in Asia are not as tall as their relatives in Africa. Their trunks are not as wrinkled and their backs are flatter. The father elephants have smaller tusks and the mothers have no tusks at all. Their ears are not as broad and are shaped very much like the map of India.

The elephants of Asia are more gentle and are more easily trained to work with men.

They are the elephants that we most often see in zoos and in circuses doing tricks.

They are very smart and learn quickly. When treated kindly they seem to enjoy doing what their trainers want them to do. But if the trainer treats them cruelly he should watch out. The elephants will pay him back.

When Little Elephant is five years old he starts to school to learn his lessons. He, too, has a schoolmaster. This schoolmaster, who is kind and patient, is an old elephant of fifty years. He is called a *koonkie.*

A training pen, which serves as a school room, is built of logs. It is just the size of a small elephant. The Burmese boy who is to be Little Elephant's oozie tries to coax him into the pen by offering him a banana.

But Little Elephant is suspicious. He flips his trunk and starts to run away. Then the old koonkie puts his big head against the stubborn little fellow's rump and pushes him into the pen.

When Little Elephant is shut in the pen, the oozie offers him another banana. But he kicks and bawls and will not take it. He acts like a sulky child. How good the banana would taste! Finally he snatches it and stuffs it in his mouth as if to say, "Oh, well I may as well eat this and make the best of things."

Now his first lesson begins. He must learn to let his oozie ride him. The oozie is lowered by ropes from above, and Little Elephant is surprised to find him sitting on his head.

How he screams and kicks and bucks!

Then the oozie is pulled up by the ropes. When Little Elephant becomes quiet he is given another banana and again the oozie is lowered to sit upon his head. Again he kicks and bawls. This is done over and over and over again until at last he lets the oozie sit on his head without making any fuss.

He has learned his first lesson.

Then a block of wood is lowered onto his back. Little Elephant bucks like a bronco. He sits down. Maybe that will get the horrid thing off his back. When he sits down the oozies shout, *"Hmit!* (Sit down!)."

Then the block is lifted and he stands up. *"Tah!* (Stand up!)" the oozies shout.

Up and down, up and down Little Elephant goes as the block is lowered and then lifted until at last he comes to know that *"Hmit!"* means "Sit down" and *"Tah!"* means "Stand up!"

When evening comes the oozie sits on his head and with his hand he presses on Little Elephant's back.

"Hmit!" his command rings out and Little Elephant obediently sits down.

A great cheer goes up from the oozies. He has learned his lessons well. They tell him what a splendid elephant he is.

Day by day Little Elephant learns new lessons. He learns to walk quietly with the old koonkie. He learns that when his oozie leans back he must halt, and when he leans forward he must kneel. He learns what all the movements of his oozie mean, and when he is eight years old he has learned to travel through the jungle with a light pack on his back.

When he is nineteen years old he becomes a worker in the teak forest.

He is a fine, big elephant with gleaming tusks. His oozie loves him and names him Maung Shwe, which means Mr. Gold. They will be good friends all their lives.